About the Author

Thirty-two-year-old mother of two, who enjoyed
reading and writing from a young age… art, drama,
painting and dance have always been my passions and I
truly thrive in those fields.

Naked

Taleka White

Naked

Olympia Publishers
London

www.olympiapublishers.com
OLYMPIA PAPERBACK EDITION

A CIP catalogue record for this title is
available from the British Library.

ISBN: 978-1-80074-360-1

First Published in 2022

Olympia Publishers
Tallis House
2 Tallis Street
London
EC4Y 0AB

Printed in Great Britain

Dedication

I dedicate this book to those who have been silenced
and needed a voice.

Acknowledgements

I thank my children for giving me the strength to write this book.

Broken

You're not meant to touch me there and I know it, yet I say nothing.

I just stand there while you grope me, while you break my heart and my spirit. Your hands are so cold as they brush over my wet nipples, they erect ever so slightly, does that mean that I like it? So much is running through my mind while you molest me, while you take the innocence from me, but the biggest question that remains is what the fuck are you thinking? I'm twelve and you're forty… Plus, you've been trusted to look after me. What kind of man does something like this? Does the thought of my tightness turn you on? Or do you look at me and see the beauty I will become? Because of you I became something so ugly, I look in the mirror and struggle to see me. All I see is a deep sadness, the hurt and pain you caused, the many men I've let in trying to find that piece of me that you took. I just see broken.

Growing up in a typical West Indian family, children are to be seen and not heard. That wasn't me; you saw that and took advantage. Grandma's house had to be the second-best place to be, I had my uncles, my dad and of course grandma. What kid doesn't love granny's house? I got to stay up late, eat around the clock… food; always so much food. Granny would be in the kitchen at one a.m. frying up those dumplings, mixing that batter for the banana fritters. Let's be honest, you get to do everything that mummy doesn't allow. Fifteen years later with two kids of my own, where did she find the time and the energy? My sister and I spent so much time in that house; after school, weekends, birthdays, even Christmas day. Other than nanny's, this was the place I wanted to be.

Then you came along.

Why was I calling you uncle? I was old enough to know you weren't my dad's brother, plus, you were sleeping in the same bed as granny. You took my spot and now I had to sleep in the back room, where the washing was on the bed, piled high to the ceiling, and there was this annoying draft that used to flow through the room. It was scary; none of us ever wanted to sleep back there, we'd even opt for the floor in the front room first. It was at the back of the house, I was alone but it would be completely inappropriate for me to share the bed now you were in it, but you still came looking for me didn't you! You seemed so nice. Everyone seemed to like you so why shouldn't I? You played with us, you even showed me how to play the piano with both hands, your favourite song at the time was Rise by Gabriel. We were bonding. I trusted you.

The mind is an amazing thing. I sometimes wonder if yours has blocked out what you did to me. You look like you just live life with no care or remorse. I wish I could forget, but I can't. I remember every little nasty detail and it plagues me. The days, the week, the time is all a blur but how and where. The texture of your rough hands across my breast, the warmth of your tongue in my mouth and the sharpness of your teeth as they pinched my bum cheek, I remember.

I remember.

You'd wait till the house was quiet, until I was alone. Did you know that I was scared? Did you know that I cried myself to sleep? Do you know that I still do?

Granny would leave us with you to go and do the shopping, run those daily errands, and uncle was living his life. A complete opportunist. A moment of fun for you and a lifetime of pain for me. Until you got caught, that was it I thought. It's over, they've seen you now, what are you going to do? Nothing, just laugh and send them away. They were only kids after all and what they had to say didn't matter. For a moment, I had a sense of relief. I even leaned into the kiss hoping it would egg you on just long enough for them to pop their heads around the corner, but it made no difference; you were so secure and comfortable. You knew I wouldn't say anything. Was that because you knew I was scared or because you thought I enjoyed it? Either way, you kept on going and you would have gone the whole way if you weren't stopped. What the fuck were you thinking?

My heart is racing, my palms are sweating as you pin me to the bed. This is it, right? This is what you've been grooming me for. All these weeks of touching and stroking and licking and sucking. (Now you're going to rape me.) I'm not ready for sex. It hadn't even crossed my mind before now. I mean I know that you're going to put your penis inside of me, but I don't *really* get how it works.

Then you bite me, it's so hard I'm sure I'm bleeding.

I try so hard to hold in my scream as the salt from my tears moisturises my tongue. My mouth is so dry, I can't swallow, I can't scream. Shit I don't even know if I can move. Then the door opens! I'd like to say that I scrambled away quickly but in fact it was the complete opposite. My body moved in slow motion as if the blood had left every limb and had already decided that I was not going to fight.

Everything changed after that moment. Not only had I decided that I was going to fight, I'd decided I was going to talk. I had to tell somebody; I didn't want to be raped nor did I want this to continue. If I didn't speak out now whatever happened to me next would be my fault. The words rattle around in my head but I can't seem to get them out. I lay there in bed laughing and joking with my sister as the tears roll down my cheeks onto the pillowcase. She has no idea that I'm hurting. We keep talking nonsense in bed, we know mum will be up soon to tell us to be quiet and go to sleep. I'm hoping she'll come up. Why can't she look at me and see my pain? Why doesn't she know that he's hurting me? Mummy cracks the door and pops her head in, "GO TO SLEEP, you have school in the morning." She's looking at me. I'm looking at her. I want her to see that my light's not shining. I want her to see the pain in my eyes. Why can't she look at me and tell? That's it, I've got to say something. The words are on the tip of my tongue. I can hear them in my head. It makes sense, just say it; "He's touching me."

Before I know it, the light from the hallway fades as the door slowly closes. Now she's gone I've lost my opportunity. Time seemed to stand still from that moment on. I don't know when the words left my lips or what order they even flowed, I just remember hearing her little voice say, "You got to tell mum, I'm telling!"

So many voices. Everyone had something to say but I never heard a word. The silence was loud and all eyes were on me. "It's important that we get as much information as possible, do you think you'll be able to make a statement, Sweetie?" At the time those words felt so comforting, but it made no difference, they still failed me. Twice! Poked and prodded, being touched again. I didn't even understand why — there was nothing to see except the teeth marks you left on my backside. Everyone was so angry; all they did was fight and argue. I just remember feeling like this was my entire fault. Why did I have to open my big mouth? I was always told I had way too much to say and this time my mouth really did cause trouble. Plain-clothes police officers, liaison, social services, it was all so serious and official. I had to sit there and say it over and over and over again. What you did to me, where you did it, how you did it, what I felt. What I felt was pain and anger, I was mad as hell. I spent weeks if not months listening to people talk about me, in a whisper, on the phone, behind my back. I don't recall mum saying much to me. The silence was killing me slowly. I convinced myself that everyone hated me or worse; they didn't believe me.

As human beings, we seek reassurance; we need to feel secure. I'd never felt so isolated in my life. Twelve-year-old me needed to be told, "It's OK, I believe you." All I remember is silence.

Me

I'm not a secondary school twelve I'm a primary school twelve. What I mean is; my hair was in cornrows (and not the kind you see today with some of these young ladies). If you were raised as a black woman from the '80s you'll know exactly what I mean — two-part separation with about ten plaits, half up half down. Makeup wasn't even in my vocabulary. I discovered that later on and not from lack of trying, but still couldn't dress or look like the twelve-year-old girls of today. My clothes wore me; I was tall and lanky with a slim frame. Mummy always struggled to find me clothes that fit in length as well as round the waist. My trousers were baggy (never fitted to show my figure) and my t-shirts reflected my age with the latest Disney character printed across it. Skin. Skin was never on show, my mother was a real black woman raised by an older generation of parents. Children remained children until they're not and even then, they're still *your* children. I was innocent. Pure. Untouched. Social media wasn't invented. We're talking about times when the internet wouldn't work because your mum was on the house phone chatting with your aunty all night. No Snapchat, Instagram or TikTok. My only influence would be my bigger cousins who wore their hair in four doo doo plaits and still wore tights on their head for bed. *Oh, how times have changed.*

I wouldn't go as far as saying that I wasn't into boys but boys really weren't that into me, I was a bit of a tomboy; played rough and wanted to kick ball. Flirting for me was like a paper cut in the joint of your fingers; *painful.* I wasn't the cutest girl at school and by far wasn't the popular kind. I guess I just didn't have the... the look. To be quite honest, primary school was a nightmare and school in general didn't get much better for me.

My skin was so fair that I could pass as mixed-race. I was a lovely light brown complexion (you know the colour of caramel in the Galaxy chocolate bar) and in the summer I tanned up real nice; a golden shimmer like when you put honey on your roast chicken. I could be a little pasty and pale in the winter, making me look slightly sick, but I had these big dark brown eyes and a smile that was contagious. Only problem with that was I was actually black. Not mixed—race, black. Both my parents were from the Caribbean islands. My mum was the colour of an Americano while my dad was more Mocha with a hint of milk. My fair skin was a throwback from my granny and I was still fairer than her. That contagious smile was engulfed in these thick pink lips while my nostrils allowed you to look straight up my nose. I had real black girl features. Black girls loved to hate me and mixed-race girls couldn't claim me. I was just there. I was in this place of not belonging. I didn't fit in. Making friends was always a struggle for me; I was a good kid, my heart was always in the right place but the child I was at home wasn't the child I was in school. It's as if I left my confidence at the school gate in the morning and walked into a new environment each day. If I told you I was shy and socially awkward those that know me would laugh out loud, I mean that kind of laugh that makes your cheeks ache and your belly hurt. But I was. In fact, I was bullied throughout primary school. The girls were always so mean. I could never comprehend what the other girls had that I didn't. OK so I didn't really take any pride in my appearance; my legs were always dry, my shoelaces always untied and my shirt would hang out the back. Mummy use to say I looked as though I'd been dragged through a hedge backwards — my jumper hanging off my shoulder and my sleeves stretched out passed my fingertip, but I was a good kid! The boys would laugh at my hair and say they didn't want to date a girl that had *pepper grains,* and I didn't care enough to brush them up in the mornings. Like I said, I was a primary school twelve.

There were times when I didn't even want to attend school. Every so often me and mummy would have a duvet day. Those were the best. We'd bunk off school and sit around watching our favourite movies, snacking on Malted Milk or Fruit Shortcake biscuits, singing along to the latest Mariah Carey or Whitney Houston song in the mirror with our hairbrushes as microphones.

Mummy was an image of perfection; her chocolate brown skin was an even tone all over, she had long dark hair that sat just below her shoulder. She stood at a short 5'4 with a slim frame just like mine. I admired her *swag* and wanted to be just like her: confident and sassy.

She took no prisoners when it came to defending and protecting her kids. No bully was left unscathed from her sharp slick tongue. No teacher, no parent, no child could infiltrate the shield that she placed around us. I later took that shield and made it my greatest weapon and my biggest weakness.

Then I met her.

She was fair (fairer than me) with long dark brown hair that she wore in a low pony, plaited down to the small of her back and the ends used to curl under. Unlike me she was actually mixed-race and had a place of belonging, but she wanted to hang with me. I'd finally made a friend! One I'd go on to call my family. She was better presented than I was. She was always a bit of a girly girl. She taught me to stuff my sports bra with tissues so that the boys would look at me and she'd try to redo my hair so it didn't look so nappy. The boys loved her. She was beautiful, a little thicker than me but she had what I didn't... the look. She was definitely the popular kind., Girls hung out with her from both classes and all races; we weren't even in the same class. I remember her teeth being perfectly straight and white. I don't know about you, but at twelve I had two big front teeth that made my whole face look goofy.

We hung in the playground gossiping about the mean girls or the latest cute boy. We'd got to that stage of having "boyfriends" — you know the kind that sat next to you on the carpet in class or stood next to you in the line. I don't even think we held hands. Kiss Chase was the game of the day where we'd take it in turns to chase the one we crushed on, to only *not* kiss them if we caught them. I finally had a friend and a "boyfriend"... which apparently you shared with your friend. I should have known from then that she couldn't be trusted.

Primary school was drawing to an end, and I was finding myself — still a little reserved and shy when left exposed but I'd made a friend that I spent a lot of time with outside of school. You see, our parents became very close. I'd never had a friend that wasn't blood related. I grew up with my cousins and siblings being my friends, but this girl's mummy took a liking to her and her mum. They'd spend many nights talking on the phone about their boyfriends, the latest rave they were going to on the weekend and mostly what they'd plan to do together *tomorrow*.

She was my best friend, sleepovers, shared bath waters… you name it, we did it. Wherever she was you'd find me and if you saw me, she wasn't far behind.

Life was feeling good. I couldn't have asked for a better end to my junior years. We only had a few weeks left; summer holidays were fast approaching, and we'd even got into the same secondary school. But no one saw what was coming next. At one of the most paramount times in my life, when I needed to be confident and know myself, you came along and you turned out my light!

Mummy went on holiday and left me and my sister at granny's — nothing unusual about that, she was a young granny and school was about a fifteen-minute walk from hers. Perfect really. We often stayed weekends and holidays there, so this time was no different. Granny had been spending time with this man that had come over from Jamaica. Now I was a pretty clued-up kid but I did not realise that they were an item until I saw him in her bed one night and was told I wasn't sleeping in her room. He was pleasant enough. If anything, he was a little quiet and reserved from what I remember. Before long granny was popping to the shops and running errands and leaving us all at home with him. Makes sense I guess — I know how hard it is to get ready with kids in tow, just to grab some dinner.

I was in my last year of primary school. Puberty had set in and I had these little swollen nipples that would poke through my t-shirt and hurt like fucking hell when they brushed on anything. I was yet to grow any hair on my mini, but my legs were pretty hairy. I hadn't started my period yet but just had sex education so was fully aware of what to expect and how babies are made. Most of my time was spent playing with my little sister and my little uncle who were six years old and if not them, I had one friend that I made at school and her mum and my mum subsequently became best friends, so she just became family automatically. I had no social life (not like the twelve-year-olds of today). It was completely different; my friends were my cousins. Point being my lashes weren't on fleek, my eyebrows were not sharp and my nose was not contoured. Not that it would justify his behaviour, I just draw reference to my innocence and my innocent look. I was a 'plain Jane' average twelve-year-old.

I don't remember the dates or the times but I remember the first time.

Granny had told me to get a shower while she ran up the road to go do something or another. The bathroom was through the back of the kitchen and the house was always cold (you know that painful cold, the one that penetrates your skin like a thousand needles). I'd always take at least my underwear with me just to try and preserve some of the heat for the walk back to the bedrooms. I'd gone through and was in the shower before she left so when I heard the bathroom door open, I wasn't alarmed or taken aback as granny would sometimes pop in and out the bathroom when us kids were washing up to make sure we were doing it correctly and, more importantly, doing it at all and not just standing there while the water ran. I glanced back towards the door and didn't hear anything, no words… nothing. Before long the shower curtain was pulled back and it was him standing there looking at me. I froze but didn't cower. I wasn't entirely sure if him being in there was wrong or not — kids of my era weren't really taught privacy. In fact, it was more like because we didn't pay any bills in the house, privacy was a luxury we weren't entitled to. I did wonder however, what the fuck he wanted and why he was just standing there looking at me. Eventually he told me to continue washing and make sure I did a good job, so I did. He then leant in and turned me to face him. At that moment the water felt like it ran cold all down my back. My mouth immediately dried up and this feeling of what I can best describe now as anxiety, (but at the time felt like I wanted to shit and vomit all at once) ran through me. I didn't resist or speak I just turned; now we were eye to eye. Anything else he said sounded like my whole head was submerged under water and all my other senses were heightened. He stood so close to me I could smell his breath — he'd been eating some form of fried food; either a dumpling or maybe fritters. I could smell the oil mixed with the batter.

I stepped out of the shower onto the cold floor and reached for my towel. As I began to wrap it around myself, he reached out and pulled my hands back open. He began to touch my nipples with a twisting motion. I remember thinking his fingertips were so rough and my nipples were so sore. I want to say that I spat on him, or I screamed and ran out, but I didn't. I just stood there. I let him touch me. Then he leaned in again. This time he pressed his mouth against mine and held it there. No, I didn't move. I didn't bite him. I let him. I think I even smiled a little, I was so scared and confused I didn't know how to react. I closed my towel and was able to make my excuses to leave the bathroom; I guess he was just testing the waters because that was only the beginning.

That week felt like it lasted a lifetime. The constant touching whenever someone left the room. Any moment he could grab, he was forcing his tongue down my throat or caressing my private parts. It felt so slimy and wet, nothing like what I imagined my first kiss would be like. I'd imagined that I was going to fall in love with the boy of my dreams and he was going to hold my hand and stroke my hair before leaning in and gently kissing my mouth. I'd seen it on all the black movies my mum and pops used to watch. Not like this. I didn't like it; I didn't like him. I just wanted him to stop. But he didn't. Every day it just got a little bit worse, more intense. By now my body language was saying 'no' but I still hadn't built up the strength to push him off or say that one little word. Stop! My days got longer, and I was counting down the minutes till mummy came back. I couldn't wait to escape. I just wanted to run through that door. I sat and I waited while I cried. Granny was oblivious, as I watched her go to bed with this man — the man that touched me during the day and slept with her at night. Did he touch her like he touched me? Did he kiss her like he kissed me? How could one person be so calculated?

Thick, warm and wet. I remember the texture of his tongue as it penetrated my mouth. He'd always force it right to the back of my throat, making me dribble a little. My eyes wide open, blinking, looking up to the ceiling. My thoughts jumbled and unable to focus from the fear that possessed my body. I was weak. With every touch and every kiss, a part of me faded. It's like the person I was born to be was dying and a new resident was taking up occupancy in the shell that he had created.

I'd gone from wanting to be wanted and seen, to being his desire. Is this what they meant when they said be careful what you wish for? Surely there can't be a God? I'd asked for the boys to notice me. I wanted to be the popular kid and here I was in a house full of kids, and it was me he was craving. This wasn't what I meant — not him, not here, not now! Any faith I had in a higher being was shattered at that very moment, how could God watch him do this to me? All those prayers I'd prayed, my christening, blessings to protect me as a child of God, bible classes I'd sat through with my nan — pointless!

I stood alone and ME was created.

Because of You

Pain, anger and rage, something happened to me. I spent the six weeks holidays pretending to be OK. Have you ever been so scared that you don't want to sleep? Every night was the same nightmare; you coming into my room and touching me. I'd dreamed before but nothing like this, your words were so clear and persistent. Your touch imprinted on my body. I knew the feeling before your skin even touched mine. Our bodies becoming one, as the warmth of your breath trickled down my neck and the pressure from your awakening penis pressed against my vagina. You wanted to feel her moisture but it wasn't yours to have. I can feel my heartbeat in my head. The heaviness in my chest made me breathless. My eyes are glazed with the tears that fill them as I work myself into a panic. I refuse to let them fall; you don't deserve anything else from me. You've taken enough already. A cold chill ran down my thigh and stuck to my dampness, my sheets are sticky from sweat as I try to fight. But you don't stop. Your hands run over my curves, gripping my flesh for your added pleasure, you love the control. Your dick hardens with my every pant and squirm. My nipples are hard and my clit is throbbing. I don't want you but I can feel you, my body had learned that it had an appetite for sex.

Woken by the vibration from the base in the speakers, I could hear the words of Beres Hammond echoing through my walls. Why so loud? The indignation that filled my body as I was woken again by the sounds of music. Now don't get me wrong, I *love* me some music — it's my body's language. Lyrics would caress my skin as the beat and melody rocked me back and forth gently, but this was belligerent... or was it? Where's the respect that I was sleeping? OK so I don't pay any bills in the house; but does that mean I have no rights in the place I call home? Every weekend I'll be woken out of my sleep with no prewarning, like my heart wasn't pounding for the entire night already. I was mad, big mad. I'd made a decision that no one was going to take advantage of me again, everybody was going to listen! Stand up and pay attention. I wanted to be heard, I was ready to fight!

That fight started at home, crazy as it may seem. I didn't know any better you see. The people closest to me had hurt me the most. My nightmares and my daydreams weren't about strangers with unidentified faces; they were the people I knew from the places I grew.

After months of loud whispers and talks in the other room, the CPS had decided that my voice wasn't worth listening to. No court case, no judge and jury, no fair trial. A group of people who didn't know me or you had decided it wasn't worth the taxpayer's money to take you to court. And just like that, it was over. I'd spoken out loud for no reason. Two families had been torn apart and the love for one another that once bound us was gone, completely severed.

I'd not seen my granny in months — the rules were, I was to have no contact with her or the house in question. I couldn't comprehend what had been put in place. I'd like to say that my intelligence surpassed me but my emotion ruled me. How could the very same people who said they didn't believe me be the said same people to keep me away from her? It wasn't her fault; she didn't make you touch me or kiss me. She wasn't even there. Surely, she believed me?

They say the mind is a funny thing and no two minds are the same but this memory, for me, is seamless. I'd heard she was now your wife. Someone who had once loved me like her own had chosen you. You weren't in jail or homeless, you'd taken my space in the bed... permanently! I'm not one for clichés but I'm told there are five stages of grief and I'd entered into denial. Here is where I'd live for the next twenty years, completely unaware of the impact you'd had on me. There are a few blank spots I'm sure someone somewhere would be happy to fill in for me, but this day, this day changed the game.

As I walked to collect my sister from school, sporting my new secondary school uniform, I heard the wolf whistles, with my skirt rolled up passed my knee to show more leg and my shirt unbuttoned to reveal my cleavage. I loved the attention. The boys on the bus home from school had finally noticed me and the men in their cars caught themselves looking twice, I'd finally learned how to use what you saw in me. I heard my name (or an abbreviation of some sort). It was a familiar voice. "TT."

Looking back then and now I wish I'd kept walking. It was granny on her school run to pick up my uncle. Great, some time alone and I'm sure she's got some form of snack in her bag (banana fritters or cheese and ham toasties, she was good for that). But today was different. Something was bubbling inside of me, my palms were sweating and my mind was unsettled. I needed to understand for myself; I'd heard you hadn't moved out and I heard you'd got married but there was no ring on her finger, and she acted as though nothing had happened, so that can't be right. As the words left my lips to question her love, her loyalty, I immediately regretted it. Her high-pitched screech pierced my ears as she dismissed me and cast my feelings aside, "Chuh," she yelled, "Forget about all that." What! Forget about it? Your boyfriend molested me, your grandchild, and you married him! My stomach turned and my mouth watered. I could taste the salt in my cheeks, swallowing hard as to not bring up the bile that sat heavy on my chest. There was no processing; I heard what I heard — this bitch, not only did she not acknowledge my pain she dismissed me. Not only did she keep him she married him. Not only did she not believe me she stopped me from healing.

Tears flooded my face and my nose ran into my mouth. I licked my top lip again, the salty flavour graced my tongue as I yelled at her. I couldn't believe what she was saying, my *grandmother* — I was *her* baby's baby. She was meant to protect me if my mother couldn't. Yet here she was rejecting me. What did he have that I didn't? Why not me? A question I still ask. My face flushed hot and red with resentment and disappointment, all my features swelling. There was no denying I'd been crying with all those black girl features amplified.

Walking through those school gates was terrifying, like I was back at age ten being tormented by my demons. All eyes were on me and this time it was for the wrong reasons. "Are you OK, Sweetie? Is everything OK?" The words blurred and merged with hers. Here I was amongst strangers who could see my pain, but she couldn't. Every word she said had burrowed in my chest like a tick, deeply embedded. My loved one, the one I'd pined for, for so long, had cut me deeper than any shards could have. The numbness I succumbed to, the feelings that transpired that day became the energy that fuelled me.

I could bore you with what happened when I got home but it was more cussing and yelling that sounded like white noise to me. Everyone was so angry and hurt for me, but I wasn't helping. I'd lost my identity and I was going to spend the rest of my life trying to get it back. Everything else was irrelevant.

I'd decided that no one was going to hurt me again. I became an empty vessel, and my body was just the host. I didn't live here and the demon that took my place was ready for the fight. Most children are taught to defend themselves, but the general rule was 'if someone hit you, hit them back'. I couldn't process and comprehend that theory as it may be the only hit. If I felt I was threatened or under attack, that shield of armour I acquired was my greatest asset. Was I wrong to protect myself? Words are a powerful thing and I had learned to use mine: demoralise, degrade, victimise… you name it, I'd mastered it. The host had found its own physical strength and I'd become physically impenetrable and emotionally impassable.

My life spiralled on. Empathy didn't exist, and compassion wasn't in my vocabulary. I wanted what I wanted and when I wanted it and anything in my path would be demolished. I was in pain and the world was going to know, I just didn't care! There was no exception to the rules. I was a rebellious teen on a mission to find myself and as far as I was concerned, my assignment was solo. My parents couldn't control me and my friends couldn't keep up with me, I was prepared to lose it all to find myself. *"I've been through my darkest time alone." I didn't need anyone?*

Locked in a room with only my thoughts, a book and single blanket (that didn't cover me from head to toe), my own solitude was welcomed. The noise of the other inmates yelling for attention and the slamming of the doors and bolts were the only things accompanying me. I couldn't understand what all the fuss was about — my cell was the safest I'd felt in years. I didn't wonder how I got here or why me, I knew why, it was all part of the mission I faced in this world and it took no prisoners. So I slept and I slept and learned that peace of mind was worth the fight.

My journey hadn't even begun, and I didn't even know it. Someone once told me I *would* get there but I was set on getting there the hard way. What was once a massive insult has now become my life as I leap over every hurdle and embrace the race. I realise I am who I am, and I am *me* because of you.

No Place Like Home

Have you ever felt complete security that you slept through the night without a stir; your mind relaxed to a place of immense blissfulness? Nothing can touch you, not a sound can wake you, and not a demon can haunt you? I hadn't! I should have been dreaming of my latest crush or the trip to the cinema I had with friends over the weekend but instead I was drowning in my own thoughts, my own nightmares. I spent my days trying not to think about you and what you had done to me, and my nights trying to figure out how you slept knowing what you did to me. There was no escape, I was haunted. Time is a great healer (here we go again with the cliché), bullshit, time did nothing for me other than give me more unanswered questions. What was your life like now? Are you doing that to another girl or boy even? Was I special? Did you love me? Are you missing me? Wait, what? Why would you miss me? You tried to destroy me; my very being you tried to ruin. Surely a monster like you was incapable of any feelings or emotions. Savage — the real definition of a vulture. Sometimes I'd lay in bed praying that when you were inside of her, my face is what you'd see curtailing your orgasm. Haunting you, while she kissed on your thighs and sucked your penis, so that it stayed flaccid, hoping that my pain radiated through to you both in your most intimate moment. Why should you be free? I was stuck with you as a memory imprinted on me. We were bound whether I liked it or not. We shared something that I could never share with another.

I'd like to say that my life calmed and my peace of mind was found, but that would be a lie. Let me take a step back for you.

Secondary school here I come… a place that's meant to be filled with friends, never-ending experiences, tears and laughter. "LOL" mine was over before it began. Five pound draws before school and a bottle of 20/20 by the age of fourteen. I had no rules and if I did, I'd broken them until I made my own.

I was a leader. I had my army and they followed without interrogation. Well so it appeared… in fact I was completely lost. I had my one true friend that I'd carried from primary school and, little did she know, I wanted to be more like her. She was a place of comfort; a familiar face (I'm not a fan of the unknown), she was safe. We spent many nights talking on the phone, my inner-most, darkest secrets I shared with her. There wasn't anything she didn't know. From the boy I crushed on to the latest trainers I wanted, even how much I hated my parents and planned to leave as soon as I reached sixteen. The typical MO of a teenager, no? Whatever it was, we did it and we did it together.

First on the list of things to do was drugs, let's get high! Now let me make one thing clear; doing drugs was never something I'd even thought about, but weed, weed was different. I had this misconception that smoking cannabis wasn't doing drugs — it was a normal part of life amongst the black community, like it was our God-given right to try it, do it, and enjoy it. So why was I going to be any different? The back of the playground smelt like cannabis and tobacco, and I wanted to fit in with that crowd. So, my master plan was to steal the half-smoked spliff I saw in the ashtray before I went to bed, while hers was to steal the bag she saw stowed away in the freezer. That ought to do it, right? The walk to school that morning had to be one of my best teenage experiences as I puffed away on a burnt-out spliff, flinching every time the heat touched my lips, giggling at the squirrel chasing the nut. By the time I made it to the playground the munchies had taken over and my snack bag was gone, now I was ready to *sleep*.

Class was what these young folk called a myth; the teacher was moithering me to pay attention but I just couldn't stay focused. Have you ever tried to understand French when you're high as fuck? It's what I imagined animals hear when their owners are talking to them... "blah blah blah." And the rest. I was watching the clock, waiting for break so I could get my next fix — is this what nittys feel like chasing their high? The bell rang and I was out, rushing to the back of the playground to bill my next joint. My friend was already there waiting. She had a Tesco bag and was going around the year elevens, letting them dip their hands in. What was in the bag? As I got closer, I heard someone say, "That girl's giving away free weed." Wait, what? Surely, she couldn't be that stupid? I approached her with a suspicious mind and grabbed her arm to pull her to me. Looking in the bag all

I could see was bud after bud.

"For fuck's sake!"

Now I wasn't the smartest kid, but I was sure there was some law she was breaking by distributing these goods. We exchanged a few words as I expressed my concerns on her choice of action, and I questioned where she got so much weed from in the first place. She didn't take too kindly to me raining on her parade and my questioning was quickly shut down by a sharp slick response. I humbled myself, took a bud and had an older guy build me a spliff. As I sat on the grass enjoying life, smoking my worries away, I glanced around at my surroundings, at peace with my environment. Yeah, if this is how weed made you feel, I could fuck with this. My eyes fell upon this guy from my class; big guy, 6 foot and 280lbs at least. There was some sort of commotion going on around him. As I dragged myself to my feet, sliding down the hilly grass edge, I realised that the commotion involved my friend. This guy had his hand all over her, she was *frass*: stumbling, slurring her words, eyes rolling back in her head. And him, he had his fucking hand up her skirt. I marched over and parted the crowd that was egging him on, forcing and pushing my little five-foot frame through to get to the centre. My mouth was watering and I felt sick to my stomach. Here we go again, another man taking advantage of a woman while all these people stand back and watch. My body became fuelled with rage as his face mutated into my abuser's. I could no longer see my reality, once again I was submerged by my own demons. All I saw was *you*; your face, your hands. I heard your laugh and saw your smile, all over her. My body was so enraged that I didn't see her smiling, or the other kids laughing; I didn't see two consenting teenagers having fun. I just saw red! I couldn't let this happen, not again. You can't hurt someone I love; I wouldn't wish my pain on my worst enemy. My face flushed with rage while my skin was dampened by a cold sweat as the adrenaline kicked in. I balled up my fist and punched him straight in his face!

"Oh shit," was the common words my ears honed in on as I pulled her out of your arms. But that's just it, they weren't your arms. They were the arms of a fourteen-year-old opportunist and I'd just punched him in his face for *shooting his shot*. I couldn't tell you what happened between that and the bell, I just remember going back to class high with sore knuckles. Before long, myself and my friend were being summoned out of class. We took a long walk down to the sports hall, accompanied by the female PE teacher. I didn't know they had the right to pat you down, but she did just that. She pulled out a lighter from a blazer pocket and that was the start of complete and utter chaos.

Suspended from school pending investigation! Statement upon statement, snitches; shit these kids didn't need pressure or the police, just tell them you were calling their mums and they'd sing. "Drugs on the premises, with the intent to supply." I can hear the words ringing in my ears as my mum screamed them at me. Huh, what? All I did was smoke a spliff and got high and loose. My head in my hands, looking across the table at my friend as our parents hovered over us. "Here, seeing as you want to smoke weed, here smoke this." You got to be kidding me, this shit only happens in movies. Our parents were young, and I can only guess this was some kind of strategy to put us off smoking for life… look at it this way, one of us is still smoking now and the other still doesn't know how to bill it. I refused as my friend lit up her joint and puffed away. Question after question as I glared at her, waiting for her to come clean. Loyalty is embedded in me like a gene, the words would never leave my lips, but I mean shit, save me… help your girl out a little. But yet nothing!

We were excluded from school permanently and if that wasn't punishment enough, my mum had grounded me until I was accepted back into mainstream (which I'd been informed could potentially be never). Friends are supposed to be family that you choose, protect you and guide you, support you through your hard times, but not this one; she was sent by the devil to test me. Someone once told me, "When you're starving, you'll eat off any plate," and that was me with her. I never had a friend that I'd made and kept; the love was real. There wasn't anything I wouldn't do for her. The next few months were epic; we snuck around while our parents worked, played dead when our tutor knocked and snuck boys in, got high and drank cheap vodka and 20/20. I can't relate to those recent Insta memes about my high school years but I was *living my best life*. As long as I had her, the rest didn't matter. I was stuck in a trance that was fuelled by her acceptance. But nothing lasts forever and that's a lesson I'm still learning.

Time passed and our parents pushed for us to get back

into school. Things changed as reality set back in. But this time I was alone — we had no choice but to attend different schools and I was back in a place of solitary. She was going to be fine (making friends was never her issue) but here I was, lost once again and this time without my right-hand man. I don't know if I was just jealous or we drifted, but I was no longer her first choice. Weekends would come and her time would be spent with another — some girl I'd never heard of or a boyfriend I was yet to meet. All I knew was I needed to make a change and take that leap.

So, I did. I branched out and started to socialise with the local kids. There were a few girls in my area that had been hanging about throughout the summer, so I reached out and played out till I was accepted. I mean it wasn't that bad, but these girls were a lot more forward than we were. We're talking sex and sleepovers at boys' houses, ha! I could just about get every other weekend at the cinema with a girlfriend (as long as my parents dropped me off and picked me up). But a girl got to do what a girl got to do, right? So I would fit in, I said what I needed to, dressed how needs must and kept quiet when I had no clue. For once I was the prettiest girl in the bunch — not that I saw it, but I'd started to grow up. My long hair and fair skin were finally playing their role, but I never realised it was the reason I was accepted by my peers. I was the bait. The face of the 'click', yet treated like a reject. These girls were 'man-hungry' and were out on the hunt. Whenever they met a new guy, it was, "Come round and meet my friend; she's pretty and she's single," and there I was entertaining some road man with sagging

37

pants that smelt like cannabis and sweaty balls.

I'll never forget the day that I met him. The girls had said they were setting me up on a blind date (so it was only right I called in my right-hand man) but before I could go, I had to wash the family car. So here I am spit-shining that shit to secure my freedom for the day, and he walks round the corner dressed in a baby blue tracksuit looking fly. Dropping the rag, I screamed, and I ran inside. Nothing could make me go back out there in my house clothes. He couldn't see me like this. I was prepared to give up all rights to my freedom for the weekend, but nothing could make me go back out there looking like a house slave. So, I gave my parents the plead and rushed upstairs with my friend to share the bath water — I couldn't keep this boy waiting too long, he was too fine for that. We washed and dressed, hair slicked, trainers fresh and stepped out (with our parents up to date with our location, estimated time of arrival and return).

OMG this boy was so *fine*. I'd had crushes before but none like this. His yellow skin shone in the sun while his perfect white teeth melted me. He had no manners; he stood at my parents' door with his pants sagging and head tilted to the side a little, looked me up and down before draping his arms over my shoulder and walking away with me. Any common sense I had was washed away in the bath I'd just taken. I wanted him and he wanted me, he was mine and I was his. We rode the tram to the fun fair and spent the whole time, lip locking, with his tongue down my throat and my pussy throbbing. This is how my first kiss was meant to feel. For once I engaged sexually and you weren't the thing on my mind. 'Love at first sight' has always been a cliché that's debatable, that shit happened to me twice! This boy was my first love, my first heartbreak, my best friend and my worst enemy and fifteen years later he's still as relevant now as he was then.

He became my peace. We'd talk on the phone falling asleep, only to wake up and continue the conversation. I vaguely remember an £800 phone bill my parents grounded me for. I didn't care, for once I had something everyone else wanted. He was pretty light skinned with freckles, his light brown eyes would glisten in the sun and his smile, his smile made any girl weak. The girls locally were going crazy for him, but he was chasing me. They offered themselves to him, those so-called friends of mine had no boundaries. I learnt the girl code from a young age and I could never date a guy that my friend already had.

Summer was here and in full swing. Mummy had gone to work and left me and my sister home. The rules were not to go out while she was at work; I never listened and often walked up to my friend's house to see what she was doing. Her mum gave her the same set of rules and we'd take it in turns to break them. But this day was different. She was very stand-offish. She kept telling me that she couldn't stand and talk with us because her mum wouldn't be happy, how she had chores to do before her mum came home. I could feel something was up (that woman's intuition is real, and you're born with it). I had to know why she was acting up. We told each other everything. So, I made my excuses to get into the house; told her I needed the bathroom. I ran straight up the stairs and looked around. Everything seemed normal except this giant teddy bear she had — it was out of place and all the stuffing was leaking over the hallway floor. I quizzed her on it. In the ten years we'd been friends, that bear hadn't moved. I reached down to move it. "Don't. You'll just make more of the stuff fall out." Made sense to be fair so I left with no more to say. We walked home cussing about her attitude and what she was up to and how she felt she had the right to refuse us entry. We were family; we slept there, we atc there.

My phone rang, which threw me out of my rant. My eyes lit up when I saw his name, my boo, my babes, was calling. Nothing else mattered now. We did small talk as he melted me with his seductive voice and he went on to tell me how nice I looked today.

"How do you know I look nice; you haven't seen me?"

"Yes, I have, I've got eyes everywhere."

I wasn't buying whatever he was selling so I brushed it off and tried to move the conversation on, and then he began to tell me I was with my sister to which I quickly responded with, "I'm always with her."

"You have on a pink rah-rah skirt and pink fuck me boots."

My heart skipped a beat as I spun round looking for him; he'd definitely seen me but where was he? I giggled nervously as I admitted my defeat in this conversation and asked him where he was.

"Where did you see me? Why didn't you say hi?"

"I was at your friend's house!"

My mouth dried up and my heart raced. He must have been having me on, I mean what would my boyfriend be doing at my girlfriend's house without me? And why would she lie and keep it from me? Tears began to roll down my face, as he gave me every detail of the conversation I had with her. He told me he'd hidden behind the giant bear, with sweating palms, anxious that I was going to pull it and discover him. He told me how he had laid her on her bed and broke the zip on her jeans trying to get in her knickers. He told me how he pulled her panties to the side to discover her moistness and how she moaned when he forced two fingers deep inside her opening. He told me how he could still smell her on his hands…

But I was still shocked seven years later when he came out of prison and left me for the girl that sent him to hell in the first place. And again, struggled to put the pieces back together when our wedding was postponed due to the pandemic, but he left me anyway for a girl he met at our engagement party. Fifteen years, four kids, two years in prison, real tears and real pain, unconditional love, six affairs with real heartbreak and heartache, with nothing left to show for it other than a few memories. I could waste a chapter on telling you why I forgave him so many times, how the sex was great and nobody had moved my body the way he had. How he raised my son I had with another man like his own, or how I wanted for nothing while he was in jail… but he doesn't deserve the recognition so I won't tell.

"When you're hungry for love you'll eat off any plate."

Love never found me like that again; I found it so easy to walk away. One man had my heart from fifteen and the rest struggled to pry it from his grip. I came close to finding comfort in another, lying beside someone I could truly see a future with. We were creating an unbreakable bond but again, I wasn't enough and he chose himself. I'd mastered the art of loving someone else but failed to find true love in me. I needed love to function… without it I was an empty vessel. I had a burning desire to be with someone who needed fixing so I didn't have to focus on fixing myself.

Lost and not sure where I was going, nan's felt like the best option. She had a spare room and could do with the extra help. Most people would describe their nan of smelling like baked goods or stale smoke, but not mine. She had a musty smell to her that had been there since she had a brain tumour removed, and raw garlic (because she swore chewing it daily would keep her immune system up and bugs away). This woman was the symbol of strength. There wasn't anything that I hadn't seen her overcome, no pain that I hadn't seen her forgive.

I'm sure I was six or seven when she came home from the hospital with her face bandaged and her nose slightly scrunched on one side, after having her head cut open to remove a tumour. She told me she would never smell again. At around ten I asked her why she stopped wearing her glasses, in which she responded there was no point as there were no glasses that could fix her condition, she was going blind. I spent my teenage years shouting at her because she lost part of her hearing, and I remember the day she stopped changing the batteries in the hearing aids because they didn't aid her hearing any more. But still she pottered around her home; cleaning and cooking, looking after her grandkids and most of all she had this unconditional love for God. Her faith inspired and angered me at the same time. How could she believe in something this much that she'd never seen or witnessed? And if he did exist, how could she be in love with someone that had allowed her to feel so much pain? I'd listen to her pray daily for hours. She'd thank God for waking her another day, ask him to continue to guide and protect her family. There wasn't a soul she'd miss out when she talked to God, even those that had wronged her. I could never comprehend how one person had so much to say to open space; I underestimated the powers behind those prayers, she protected me with every breath she took and when I was with her, I felt safe. I was home. I can't say that I spent hours telling her about my pains and problems because we hardly spoke, but she had this way of knowing when I needed her most. She'd sit on her sofa dozing off to the news or Songs of Praise, and when I asked her regularly why she didn't go up to bed and lay down, she'd respond, "Nah," in a husky voice.

I spent many years just lying on her lap while she stroked my head, her soft fingers removing my heartache as she listened to my silence and answered all my questions with no words. I was truly at peace; her prayers and her love engulfed me and kept me from harm. There's no love like a grandmother's love. Whenever I felt lost or afraid, I'd place my head on her lap and she'd sit there for hours comforting me. It was almost like she poured her strength into me so that my empty vessel would be fuelled to fight another day. As years went on, I watched her get weaker and weaker, struggling to do the simplest things for herself; too proud to ask for help from anyone, but every now and again she'd let out a sigh, "Ah child, come do something for me." She had this knack of asking me as I was running out the door or settling down to watch my favourite show. But how could I say no to the person who pumped life into me daily? I can still hear her now, "Once a man, twice a child." I'd grown up hearing her say those words, with no understanding of what she meant.

Wiping the rag over her face and behind her ears because she was no longer able to move to wash, creaming her hands and trimming her nails because she was too weak to lift her arms; I watched her, my strength, my heartbeat, still trying to pour life into me. She'd often say to me, "When me dead an' garn, what you will do?" I'd learned to block those words out; I couldn't imagine life without her. I was almost certain a piece of me would die!

My strength, my heartbeat, she lay there, and I lay with her trying to pour the life she gave to me back into her — that's the least I could do, right? Unable to walk or move on her own, she'd touch my face to identify me, and I suddenly understood what she meant by 'once a man, twice a child'. I found myself talking to God, asking for forgiveness; I was bargaining as I saw the life leaving her, one more month, just one more week, one more day, God just give me one more minute! But apparently, I had nothing worth trading.

"Nan died…"

The words echoed in my ears, but I didn't cry or scream or break down; I just made my way to her!

When a member of the royal family dies, it's breaking news, an order for the world to pay attention. Nothing else is spoken about; it's the front page, a meme, a tweet. But there was none of that for her. The world continued as normal. I travelled for what felt like hours trying to get home, wondering if the world could see my pain. I HATE YOU, God, I HATE YOU. I believe that soul mates exist but not always romantically, sometimes you meet that one person in your life that you just connect with. That perfect connection, interaction that is perfectly in sync, a bond that cannot be broken. She was my soul mate; she understood me completely and accepted me for me unapologetically. I'd lost loved ones in the past but I've never felt a pain or emptiness like this. 2016 I lost a vital piece of me. She was my life support and without her I become an empty shell. I found myself wandering the streets looking for love in all the wrong places, trying to find that missing piece of me.

As the years passed me by and the world kept on spinning, I looked at the puzzle pieces in my hands wondering what the hell I did wrong. Just as I would start to feel safe, safe from you, a sense of relief from my burdens, I'd be stripped of my haven. I finally realised there is no place like home.

Self-Destruct

Life had taught me some cruel lessons and one of them being nothing lasts forever. I never knew if this meant that I should never get too comfortable or if I should live for the moment and enjoy it. I'm an impulsive 'overthinker'; I believe everything happens for a reason and every action comes from a reaction to something, meaning there is a reason behind everything. But I do what I want when I want and most of the time, I want to do it now. But not everything that can be done should be done. I've spent many years trying to find myself, understanding my own mind and many years trying to get others to understand what makes perfect sense to me. And failed.

When I had my son, I found an unconditional love that cannot be explained in any other way than a mother's love. He was mine and no matter what I did or how I did it, he loved me for me. I set myself a mission to protect him from the things that haunted me. I didn't want him to see my hurt or my weaknesses, so I hardened. To protect him I had to protect myself. So I came back to you, to her, the very root of my pain. Forgiveness the bible says. I couldn't forgive you but I could try and forgive her. She wasn't the one that abused me, so there was room for forgiveness. I wanted my family and needed to be wanted, a place of belonging. I missed my granny and we had fun together. If it wasn't for that one incident, we'd still be together.

It's amazing how trauma has an impact on your brain. It teaches you to block and shield things that cause you pain and suffering and it's triggered by situations that occur daily, slowly releasing the poison back into the bloodstream until it suffocates you and you're forced to acknowledge and respect it. I spent years with her trying to build back that bond. Many will call me a walking contradiction, but I needed her to want me. I couldn't live with the rejection. Knowing that she picked you over me was killing me slowly, so I decided to fight for what was mine.

At first that battle seemed to be my birthdays, Christmases granny was there. I could see she would do anything to please me… was that guilt or genuine affection? My son, I gave her access to him and trusted that she'd learned from her mistakes with me. I was mad to think that an enabler had a rational mind. One, two, three… four, five, six, my son created a bond with her, and he loved her just as much as I did. Years passed and the elephant in the room was never discussed. YOU. I'd pass by the house and you would be nowhere in sight. I knew you were there but you were never spoken of. But something changed. A contentment, she'd become comfortable with my pain. You'd no longer be hiding in the back bedroom when I arrived at the house, instead you were on the sofa watching the TV. My presence in the house didn't make you uncomfortable any more. You'd decided you weren't going to hide any more. How dare you. Seven, eight, he was no longer at an age where he didn't understand his surroundings. I could hide from him in plain sight. He came home and referred to you as 'uncle' and my blood ran cold. "Mummy, uncle said..." She hadn't learnt and you didn't care. I'd allowed myself to believe that you had no interaction with my child even when under the same roof as him. I'd convinced myself that when he was there you were hiding in the back room until he was gone. But I was wrong.

When I found out my second child was a girl, you were the first thing that popped into my mind. All those years of suppressing the emotions and thoughts, you were back and this time you came back to take everything.

Sleepless nights and cold sweats, you were back haunting me, but this time I knew why. The question that rang in my head was would I send my daughter into the house that you lay? And the answer was no! My blood would start to boil at the thought of you even speaking to her or saying her name, so why did I send my son down there?

As a parent there's nothing more heart-breaking than realising that you failed your mission. I'd been sending my son to a house where I knew a known paedophile lived. I'd convinced myself that you weren't gay or that you didn't just like any little kid; it was me you wanted. But I couldn't be sure of that, how could I be? It was never spoken about.

I had to take responsibility for my actions and in turn I wanted you to do the same. In order to this I would need to strip myself bare. Expose the nerve, completely naked. Exposing you meant exposing me, but I was a complete paradox seeking understanding from those closest to me, was I asking too much? I didn't know if I understood it myself, it was just how I coped. I couldn't deal with being rejected by the very people who were causing my suffering. I couldn't let you win. So I kept my enemy close and put my child in danger while I tried to heal, but that's just it — I wasn't healing. Nothing had changed… I was still tormented by you, by her. I wanted to show you that I was fine despite what you'd put me through and I wanted her respect, constantly seeking validation from people who were no longer valid. I couldn't tell you why, it's just what I thought I needed to survive!

I'd tried to make a life for me and my kids — something stable that they could be proud of, a place called home… but something was missing.

Love.

I love my kids and I'd loved my partner, but I didn't love myself. Most of my adult life I spent time trying to fix others, giving out advice and love beyond the call of duty (whether that be platonic or romantically). I took many L's fighting for relationships that weren't worth shit to be quite frank. Friends that had done me wrong, lovers that shouldn't have passed the first date and most of all, family that didn't deserve the titles they were given. My candour nature made me like Marmite but I wanted to be loved and liked. I never truly grasped how it wasn't respected because that's all I asked from someone in life. With you I was the complete opposite: I was shy and timid, reserved and scared. I've never confronted you but it's in my nature to be confrontational. Is this why people didn't believe me or questioned and doubted my pain? I felt it was time to show the world what lie beneath but I still didn't start with you. I went to her. She was now the root of the problem. If I could only get her to see things my way, maybe you'd disappear.

Confrontation and defence my MO, a complete ambush. I sat across from her with my phone on the table secretly recording. I'd taken a risk doing this in a public place, but I'd hoped it would control my emotions and force her to act rationally. I began telling her my truths, while her face scrunched into an emotional bind and her mouth dried up, swallowing repeatedly trying to relieve the uncomfortable knot in her throat. The words flowed from tongue so poetically, controlled and liberating. Who thought speaking of such horrific things could be so peaceful? The more she became uncomfortable the more I felt emancipated. As I told her that she lay with a paedophile every night and I knew that she knew, she stared back at me riddled with unapologetic guilt. She didn't say much, denied having complete understanding of what you did. I could see the lies behind every frown and twist of the mouth. She told me how my mother hadn't given her the information that she needed to make an informed decision on the situation, and how she believed that I was just a little girl that had a fantasy and crush on an older man. She looked me in my eyes and she lied! She'd spent the last twenty years living with a monster, condoning and fuelling his behaviour with unconditional love. And now she sat here looking at me, trying to deflect the blame onto anyone but herself. Tears rolled down her face as I told her not to worry; I didn't want anything from her, she was free. I'd like to say that they were tears of sadness but I gauged relief. Twenty years she carried this burden on her shoulders, the guilt of knowing what he did to me and trying to make it right and now she didn't have to. Twenty years I thought she didn't believe me and that's why she kept him, that's what made it acceptable for her to choose him over me. Twenty years of wishing she understood my pain and the hurt they'd put me through, if only I had the strength to tell her. And in twenty minutes I realised that she knew. She believed me; she saw my pain, she felt my hurt, she knew! In twenty minutes, the answers to my questions rolled down her cheek and slipped away into the corner of her mouth only to lubricate her tongue to whisper another lie. And at that moment I realised why I didn't have her respect... because I didn't respect myself. Deep down I knew she knew. Her words didn't faze me or alter my stance. I didn't become unhinged or emotional with my new revolution. I knew she knew.

She told me that she was old and life for her now was just about having someone to grow old with, to sit in a silent room and be content with just the presence of another human's energy. She told me how it was too late for her to make a change that could save my life. I kissed her goodbye and whispered, "Once a man, twice a child."

My appetite for respect had been awoken. I knew what I needed but wasn't sure how to earn it. Speaking out loud seemed to be a good start, taking my accusation back to the police so I could hear what they had to say myself. So nice and informal, don't want to be sued by the poor little victim. Be careful what you say to her, so patronising and condescending... can I even use those two words in the same sentence? I will because that's what it was — a double slap. They had no intention of helping me. I was a tick box task for the rookie feds.

"You have insufficient evidence for the CPS to consider your case." Twice!

What more do you need? You want to be there, to

watch, and see? I honestly felt at that moment that if he'd actually raped me, I would have been better off. I'd hit an all new low, rejection again. If he'd taken my virginity, forced himself into my tightness, made me bleed a little then someone would have paid attention. Maybe I would have got a conviction.

Everything around me fell apart again but this time I felt like I'd done it to myself. I couldn't bare the lies and the hypocrisy any more. Anything that smelt like betrayal or resembled disloyalty had to be cut out like the poison it was. Your title didn't matter any more. No one was exempt, it was time to protect me and mine at all costs. With my face on the floor, I kicked and screamed, fighting to get up, with a thousand feet on my back. Many had waited for the moment I fell and weren't ashamed to stand over me unmasked. Battered and bruised from the words and the actions of the ones that claimed to love me, face to face with all my demons. I'd asked God to show me my enemies and my friends and family stood tall in front of me.

My heart broke and I was responsible for my pain but it was time to hold those around me accountable.

My body and mind weak, face soaked in my own blood, vision blurred and my hearing muffled I pulled myself up. Even with my laboured breathing, some still tried to suffocate me and drown out my words. Irrelevant, unwanted, hypocrite, joke, embarrassing, unfit parent, immature, selfish are just some of the weapons formed against me while I tried to seek answers and justice!

Justice

When someone is wronged, retribution is at the top of the list of things to be done to seek compensation for one's loss. Ultimately, I wanted justice for what you did to me. Prison seemed sufficient at the time, to be locked away for a few years to pay for the crimes you committed. But it wasn't in God's plan for me to be set free from the burdens you put on my shoulders.

I look around and wonder how one person can be put through so much suffering and still stand tall. By trying to make you pay, I made myself suffer more. And in that suffering, I found my voice.

It was time to speak out loud about all the pain you'd caused. I realised that my justice was to tell the world and not keep your secret any more. By telling my truth I set myself free. There's no excuse for some of the things I've done and the pain and hurt that I've caused but you are the reason behind so many of my actions. I was on a mission for retribution; for respect and love, but the truth is, for children like me there is no **justice.** Some are strong and go on to great things while others are suffocated and drowned by their own pain. But we all have one thing in common: there will never be enough justice that this world could offer. What a paedophile does to a child breaks their spirit forever. You're either the victim or you're to blame. But you're never just you.

Because of you I'll never know who I would have become if you hadn't shaped my life for me. And the me I became was so ugly to look at, I couldn't love it. So I spent years seeking that love elsewhere, only to be rejected and betrayed repeatedly because the desperation seeped out of my pores.

I'd like to say that I found God and he led me to forgiveness, that I learned to live with my demons, and I slept through the night despite my traumas haunting me, but I'd be lying.

But I have decided that if this nightmare is going to haunt me for the rest of my life, then why should you be spared? It seems only fair that it should be shared.